To Chad, for showing me the beauty in our differences.

And to Ryan, thank you for supporting my dreams,
even the crazy ones.

The artwork for this book was created using digital media.

Designed by Evgeniya Parkina

ISBN: 978-1-7349575-0-1

byerinstrange@gmail.com

My Big Brother Ben

An Autism Spectrum Super Story

Written by Erin Strange

Illustrated by Evgeniya Parkina

Hello! My name is Max! I am 6 years old!

I live with Mom, Dad, and my big brother Ben!

Ben is 8 years old and is my very best friend.
We do everything together!

We play with puzzles, build block towers,
and swing high up to the sky!

Ben is a **SUPER** brother!

Ben, say pizza, please.

Pizza, please!

Ben makes noises and sounds to talk. It's a secret language that only I can decode. That's a **SUPER** word for understand.

Mom and Dad give Ben words to say when he needs something. He doesn't like doing that very much, but if he really wants pizza or the tablet, he will use his words.

Ben can name every star and planet in our entire galaxy! I'm serious. He knows them all! Those are the only words that Ben will say by himself. When he's happy or excited, he shouts them out and jumps up and down. I think it's **SUPER** funny!

Ben is really good at putting all his toys into categories. That's a **SUPER** word that means sorting into groups.

Sometimes, he takes food out of the refrigerator to put into color groups. Mom doesn't like that.

Ben has **SUPER** hearing and vision too! He can hear everything.

Sometimes, though, certain noises or lights bother him. He might start to scream or even hit himself. Mom says this is called sensory overload.

Mom will sometimes put a heavy vest on Ben to help him relax. He wears headphones that block out sounds too. If he starts to flap his hands and make noises like an ambulance, she will give him slime or his favorite book about outer space to calm him down.

Ben gets to go to a **SUPER** school. I go with Mom to pick him up sometimes. He can do his work on a chair that bounces or even lie under the table! He's learning to use a tablet to help him say more words like me.

I asked Mom and Dad, "When Ben starts to talk more, will we still have our secret language?" They said that no matter what voice Ben uses, we will always have brother secrets.

When we are out shopping or doing something fun, Ben likes to high-five anyone wearing the color purple and tell them the names of all the planets and stars.

Some people will stop and listen to Ben, but other people will just walk away. It doesn't bother Ben when that happens, but it makes me a little bit angry.

Dad explained to me that not everyone has a brother like Ben, so they don't know how to act or what to say. Well, I think that's nuts and everyone would smile so big if they would just listen to him. Ben is a **SUPER** friend!

Dad and Mom tell me that Ben will always need our help, even when Ben and I are grownups! They said that even though he will grow into an adult, he will need someone to drive him places, cook with him, go to work with him, and stuff like that.

They say he has Autism. They also say all Autism is different, and I'll understand more about it as I get older.

But I already know that Ben is a **SUPER**HERO!

Made in the USA
Coppell, TX
10 March 2021